mafalda

QUINO

& friends

5

EDICIONES DE LA FLOR

Quino
    Mafalda and friends 5. -5ª. ed.- Buenos Aires:
Ediciones de la Flor, 2020.
    96 p. ; 20x14 cm.

    ISBN 978-950-515-780-8

    1. Humor gráfico argentino - I. Título
CDD A867

Traducción : Terry Cullen
Revisión: Andrew Graham-Yooll
Tapa: Paula Beinstein
© QUINO
© 2007 PARA ESTA EDICIÓN Y SOBRE
LA TRADUCCIÓN BY EDICIONES DE LA FLOR
S.R.L. ANCHORIS 27, C1280AAA,
BUENOS AIRES ARGENTINA
WWW.EDICIONESDELAFLOR.COM.AR

- "I swear I'm not dead"

Paul Mc Cartney

I'M SICK OF SCHOOL! D'YOU UNDERSTAND? SICK!

SO, IT'S **FINITO!**.. I'M NOT GOING ANY MORE!

AND DON'T COME TO ME WITH YOUR ARGUMENTS, BECAUSE YOU'LL NOT PERSUADE ME!

YOU SHOULD SEE THE POWER OF PERSUASION OF MY MOTHER'S SLIPPER!

WHAT'S WRONG, MIGUELITO? WHAT ARE YOU DOING THERE?

I'M AFRAID OF THE TAX ON EVERYTHING

"Life begins at forty"

AND SO WHY THE DEVIL DID THEY MAKE US ARRIVE SO EARLY?

HE'S IN THE AREA CONTROLLING THE BALL! A MAN COMES OUT TO MARK HIM! HE GETS ROUND HIM! WATCH OUT! HE'S GOING TO SCORE!!!

SOMETIMES I WONDER IF I REALLY AM IN GOOD HANDS

LISTEN TO THIS, MIGUELITO. "MORRIS SUCGER, METEOROLOGIST AT THE UNIVERSITY OF CALIFORNIA..."

"... ANNOUNCED THAT AIR POLLUTION BY INDUSTRY..."

"... COULD WIPE OUT HUMANITY BY THE YEAR 2064..."

I WONDER WHAT I WILL DO. A LITTLE OLD MAN ALL ALONE IN A DEPOPULATED WORLD

THANK GOODNESS I WOKE UP

BECAUSE IF ANYTHING MAKES ME MAD IT IS WASTING MY SUBCONSCIOUS DREAMING NONSENSE

I DON'T UNDERSTAND WHAT COULD HAVE GONE WRONG

TODAY MY TEACHER TAUGHT US THAT TWO AND TWO MAKE FOUR

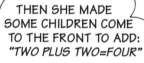

THEN SHE MADE SOME CHILDREN COME TO THE FRONT TO ADD: "TWO PLUS TWO=FOUR"

THEN WE AALLLLLLLLLLL COPIED IN OUR BOOKS: "TWO PLUS TWO= FOUR"

I SWEAR I'VE NEVER FELT SO FAR FROM *WERNER VON BRAUN*

ALWAYS THE SAME! AS SOON AS YOU TOUCH THE GROUND, THE FUN IS GONE

MY AUNTIE CLARA HAS SOME CHINA TEACUPS. BEAUTIFUL!

THEY'RE FROM WHEN THE CHINESE MADE NICE THINGS. THAT WAS BEFORE, WHEN THEY WERE NOT BAD

BUT IT SEEMS THAT LIVING IT UP IN BAD COMPANY... OH, WELL!

I DON'T KNOW WHAT COULD HAVE HAPPENED TO THOSE NICE BOYS

THIS TIME I'M SERIOUS!

I'M NEVER GOING TO SCHOOL AGAIN. AND THAT'S GOSPEL!!!

LISTEN! DO YOU SEE THIS?

VISUAL-AIDS ARE VERY MUCH IN FASHION THESE DAYS

THERE WAS SOMETHING OF A PAPAL ENCYCLICAL IN THAT LOOK

PLOP!

IT'S JUST THAT ONE GETS CARRIED AWAY ON THIS THING

VIVA ARGENTINA!

DAMN IT!

POPULAR TOUCH

WELL, IF YOU SAY IT IS *SHEEP* AND NOT *SHEEPS*, I'LL RUB OUT THE *S*. HAVE YOU GOT AN ERASER?

HERE

THANKS

SCQUICK! SCQUICK! SCQUICK! SCQUICK! SCQUICK! SCQUICK! SCQUICK! SCQUICK! SCQUICK! SCQUICK!

SCQUICK! SCQUICK! SCQUICK! SCQUICK! SCQUICK! SCQUICK! SCQUICK! SCQUICK! SCQUICK!

SCQUICK! SCQUICK! SCQUICK! SCQUICK! SCQUICK! SCQUICK! SCQUICK! SCQUICK!

MAYBE MY TEACHER IS RIGHT ABOUT THE SIZE OF MY WRITING

15

MAMA, AT WHAT AGE IS ONE OLD?

IT DEPENDS, MAFALDA. IT'S NOT SO MUCH A MATTER OF YEARS, AS KEEPING YOUR SPIRIT YOUNG

ALL RIGHT, BUT THE SPIRIT, AT WHAT AGE DOES IT START NEEDING MAKE-UP?

TELL ME, MAFALDA. WHO WAS TOM DICKENHARY?

NOBODY, MANOLITO. TO SAY "TOM DICK AND HARRY" IS TO SAY "NOBODIES"

UGH! I GOT AN ANSWER WRONG IN THE HISTORY TEST!

16

LEADING CEO LEAVES ON BUSINESS

... WHAT A LIFE!

INSTEAD OF DOING MY HOMEWORK, I'VE SPENT THE WHOLE DAY READING COMICS... THIS MUST STOP!

I CAN'T BE SO WEAK-WILLED. NO, SIR!

WHAT AM I? A MAN OR A MOUSE?

NORWAY. NOBODY TALKS ABOUT NORWAY

PEOPLE TALK ABOUT THE COUNTRIES THAT BUILD BOMBS, HAVE RIOTS, CRIME WAVES, REVOLUTIONS, RACISM, ...

BUT OF POOR NORWAY, **NOTHING**

IT SEEMS VIOLENCE HAS BETTER *RATINGS* THAN COD

HERE, MAFALDA. HALF THE NOUGAT FOR ME, HALF FOR YOU

OH, THANKS, SUSANITA

CRUNCH! CHOMP! GULP!

CRICK CROCK

MMMMMM!

CROCK CRICK

CRACK CRUNCH

DAMN MY KINDNESS!!

22

I WOULD LIKE TO CONGRATULATE ALL THOSE COUNTRIES THAT MANAGE WORLD AFFAIRS

SO I HOPE I AM GIVEN GOOD REASON TO DO SO

FRAGILE

WORLD PEACE JUST WENT BY IN A LITTLE BOX

A SAFARI!! THAT'S SOMETHING I WOULD LIKE!

I CAN SEE MYSELF FACING AN ENRAGED BEAST! WHAT WOULD I, FELIPE, DO IN THE FACE OF AN ENRAGED BEAST?

HOW SHOULD I KNOW. COWARDICE COMES IN SO MANY FORMS

DUDUM - DUDUM! DUDUM - DUMDUM! DUMDUM! DUMDUM!

CHUIIIK!

HAPPY FATHER'S DAY!

WHAT'S WRONG, MIGUELITO?

NOTHING

BUT, WHAT IS IT?

WELL, OK. I FEEL A LITTLE ANXIETY IN THIS NAIL. THAT'S ALL

DON'T TELL ME AFTER THIS THAT THERE'S NOTHING NEW UNDER THE SUN

WELL, WINTER IS HERE!

DO WE HAVE TO CALL IT "SIR"?

… AND, NEVER, NEVER, NEVER LET US BE THE HAM IN THE INTERNATIONAL SANDWICH

I'VE GOT A VERY FUNNY STORY: THERE WAS A FELLOW LISTENING TO A RECORD...

HA! HA! HA! A RECORD! THAT'S GREAT! HA! HA!

HE'S NOT FINISHED, SUSANITA

AH!

... AND ALONG COMES ANOTHER WHO SAYS: "BUT, HOW CAN YOU LISTEN TO THAT RECORD? IT'S SCRATCHED!"

SO THE MAN SAYS: WHAT'S IT TO YOU, WHAT'S IT TO YOU, WHAT'S IT TO YOU,

HEI HEI!

HA! HA!

HAA! HAA!

GO ON! AND THEN?

THE MARKET IS FULL OF THIEVES WHO CHARGE YOU AS THEY WISH. THAT'S WHAT!

HA! AND THOSE WHO CHEAT WITH THE WEIGHT? 'CAUSE THERE ARE ALSO THOSE WHO CHEAT WITH THE WEIGHT

LIES!!!!!!!!!!!

AM I GETTING YOUNGER THAN MY BODY?

STRANGE. I BENT OVER TO PICK UP A BOOK AND WHEN I STRAIGHTENED UP I FELT A STAB IN THE BACK

766

AT MY AGE I'M NOT GOING TO THINK I'M OLD. MUST HAVE JUST BEEN A DRAUGHT

OF COURSE, THAT'S IT! SOMEONE MUST HAVE LEFT A DOOR OPEN AND WITHOUT ME KNOWING...

... THIRTY-SEVEN YEARS CAME IN

EXERCISE! THAT IS THE BEST TO NOT FEEL LIKE A CREAKY OLD MAN

767

LET'S SEE SOME STRETCHES

CRACK!

CRACK?

28

IN THIS LIFE EVERYTHING IS A MATTER OF SIZE, MIGUELITO

IF WE WERE ANTS, THAT PUDDLE WOULD BE WHAT THE GREAT LAKE IS TO US

THE WHAT?

I WOULD LIKE TO ASK YOUR ADVICE, MANOLITO. I HAVE A PROBLEM

IS IT SERIOUS, SUSANITA?

SERIOUS? NO, IT'S REALLY A VERY STUPID PROBLEM

THAT'S WHY I THOUGHT THAT YOU COULD SEE IT BETTER THAN ANYONE. YOU SEE

29

COMPUTER ZK-2-09 HAS JUST FINISHED YOUR SUMS

GOOD. SEND THEM TO THE SCHOOL BY LASER MAIL

OK, NOW I'LL DO MY HOMEWORK

RIGHT!

WILLIAM SHAKESPEARE HAS FINISHED YOUR COMPOSITION ON THE COW, SIRE

OK. REWARD HIM WITH THESE PENNIES

RIGHT NOW! I'LL GO AND DO THAT HOMEWORK

YES, SIR!

I HAVE LOST 32 MEN AND A LEG, HERR MARSHALL, BUT I SEIZED FROM THE ENEMY THE MAP WITH ALL THE MAIN RIVERS OF EUROPE

THANK YOU, SCHULZ. YOU CAN GO AND HAVE ONE BUD AND NO MORE

THE DRAW IS, I'LL BE THE REFEREE; MAFALDA, MIGUELITO IS YOUR GOALKEEPER AND MANOLITO, SUSANA'S

COME ON, SUSANITA! TRUST ME, YOU'VE GOT THE MOSHE DAYAN OF ALL GOALKEEPERS!

THUMP!

30

MY GOD...
WHAT POLITICS MUST
LOOK LIKE REFLECTED
IN THIS TEAPOT

HERE, THIS IS IT.
SEE HOW FUNNY
YOU LOOK IN THIS
TEAPOT, MIGUELITO.

WAAAAA!...

IF I WERE A GIANT, NOW I KNOW WHAT I'D SEW MY BUTTONS WITH!

WAITER, MORE SALAD!

ME TOO, PLEASE

MORE SALAD, DEAR?

HOLY TERMITES!

GREAT!

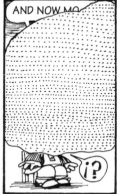

33

YOU GO SHOPPING, AND PRICES ARE TERRIBLE! NO AMOUNT OF MONEY IS ENOUGH!

THEY'RE THIEVES! THEY CHARGE YOU WHATEVER THEY PLEASE! THAT'S THE WAY THEY DO!

WHO ARE YOU TALKING TO, MAMA? ARE YOU TALKING TO YOURSELF?

I'M TALKING TO THE BUSINESSMEN, TO THE MIDDLE-MEN, TO THE AUTHORITIES WHO ALLOW...

... THEM TO ROB US. I AM NOT TALKING TO MYSELF, MAFALDA! NO, SIR!

DO YOU THINK SO, MAMA?

HURRAY FOR OUR COUNTRY!!!

HURRAY!!!

HURRAY FOR INDEPEND-ENCE!!!

HURRAY!!!

HURRAY FOR DON MANOLO'S!!!

YOU SEE THAT POOR LITTLE FLY TRYING TO GET OUT TO BE FREE? THAT'S WHAT WE HUMANS ARE LIKE, SUSANITA

AND IF WE JUST KILL IT? EEEEH?

THAT'S WHAT WE HUMANS ARE LIKE, MAFALDA

I'M GOING TO BRING A STOOL, SO WE CAN OPEN THE WINDOW AND LET THIS POOR LITTLE FLY GET OUT. I CAN'T BEAR TO SEE IT SUFFER

NOR I

ANOTHER KIND GESTURE MIGHT BE TO GIVE IT AN ASPIRIN

38

SMITH SMITH SMITH
SMITH SMITH SMITH
SMITH SMITH SMITH
SMITH SMITH SMITH
SMITH SMITH SMITH
SMITH SMITH SMITH
SMITH SMITH SMITH

SMITH SMITH SMITH
SMITH SMITH SMITH
SMITH SMITH SMITH
SMITH SMITH SMITH
SMITH SMITH SMITH
SMITH SMITH SMITH
SMITH SMITH SMITH

SMITH SMITH SMITH
SMITH SMITH SMITH
SMITH SMITH SMITH
SMITH SMITH SMITH
SMITH SMITH SMITH
SMITH SM
SMITH S

AND THERE
ARE MORE!
MY GOD!

THE SMITHS ARE
TO THE PHONE BOOK
WHAT CHINESE
ARE TO WORLD
POPULATION

HOW AWFUL!
MY GOD!...
HOW AWFUL!

IT SAYS HERE THAT
THE MACHINE GUN
WAS INVENTED IN 1861
AND THE TYPEWRITER
IN 1868! DO YOU KNOW
WHAT THAT MEANS?

HOW TO **KILL MORE
RAPIDLY** WAS INVENTED
BEFORE HOW TO **WRITE
MORE RAPIDLY.** IT'S
DEPRESSING!

DEPRESSING
DEPRESSING
DEPRESSING
DEPRESSING

THE POOR THING IS
STILL NOT USED TO
THIS WORLD BEING
THIS WORLD

40

THIS BOOK HAS SOME GOOD ADVICE, MIGUELITO: "KNOW THYSELF"

LET'S SEE

?

BUT DOESN'T IT COME WITH A MIRROR?

I CAN SEE YOU NOW, WHEN YOU GROW UP AND HEAD YOUR CHAIN OF SUPERMARKETS, MANOLITO

MY FABULOUS CHAIN OF SUPERMARKETS!!

YOU'LL HAVE MANY EMPLOYEES

HUNDREDS AND HUNDREDS OF EMPLOYEES!!

THEY'LL ALL WORK HAPPILY BECAUSE YOU'LL PAY GOOD WAGES

I'LL PAY FABULOUS WAGES!!

NOW LOOK WHAT YOU MAKE ME SAY!!!!

WHY SO MANY CALCULATIONS, FELIPE?

BECAUSE I WANT THIS PLANE TO FLY WELL

WHAT I REALLY WANT IS FOR MY LIFE TO GO WELL

THIS MAP OF THE WORLD HAS VERY PRETTY COLOURS

THERE ARE PINK COUNTRIES, ORANGE ONES, GREEN, YELLOW, LILAC...

COUNTRIES IN VERY PRETTY TONES...

... THAT HAVE NOTHING TO DO WITH THE COLOURS OF THEIR INTENTIONS

42

BUT...! THE COLOURS ON THIS MAP OF THE WORLD ARE ALL WRONG!

YOU THINK SO?

YES. LOOK AT CHINA. CHINA SHOULD BE YELLOW! ... OR RED?

BUT HERE IT IS GREEN!

THANK GOODNES, MIGUELITO! THANK GOODNESS!!

THE ONLY THING THAT INTERESTS YOU IS YOUR FATHER'S SHOP! AREN'T YOU ABLE TO THINK OF SOMETHING ELSE?

HOW CAN YOU ONLY BE INTERESTED IN BUSINESS AND MONEY?

WHAT ABOUT AL THE OTHER BEAUTIFUL AND IMPORTANT THINGS? WHAT ARE THEY?

SUPERFLUOUSITIES!

"PROBLEM: IF IT TAKES ONE BRICKLAYER 1/2 A DAY TO BUILD 2 MTS OF WALL, HOW MANY METERS COULD HE BUILD IN 3 DAYS?"

LET'S SEE. 3 DAYS MAKE 6 HALF DAYS, SO THEN...

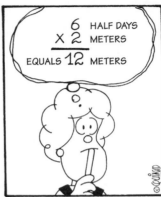

$$\begin{array}{r} 6 \text{ HALF DAYS} \\ \times\ 2 \text{ METERS} \\ \hline \text{EQUALS } 12 \text{ METERS} \end{array}$$

Answer: he would build 6 or 7 metres, because in this country nobody wants to work.

WHEN YOU FLIP THROUGH THE DICTIONARY YOU ALWAYS LEARN SOMETHING NEW

TODAY, FOR EXAMPLE, I FOUND THAT "SHUFFLE GAIT" MEANS THE SHORT, QUICK STEPS OF DONKEYS AND OTHER ANIMALS

WELL? WHAT'S THE MATTER?

I WANT TO TELL YOU, MAFALDA

IF YOU EVER HAVE ANY KIND OF PROBLEM, COME AND ASK MY ADVICE, BECAUSE I, WITH GREAT PLEASURE, WILL TRY TO HELP YOU

AND DON'T THANK ME... NO. I BEG YOU!

BECAUSE I JUST LOVE PEOPLE TO GIVE ME A CHANCE TO MEDDLE IN THEIR LIVES

I'M THIRSTY, MAFALDA. DO YOU HAVE A DROP OF "PEPSI"

THERE'S "COCA-COLA", MIGUELITO. I'LL BRING YOU SOME

NO. LEAVE IT. IF THERE'S NO "PEPSI", DON'T BRING ME ANYTHING

COME ON, MIGUELITO! AFTER ALL, THEY ARE BOTH THE SAME! AND ANYWAY, "COCA-COLA" IS BETT

A MATTER OF OPINION! I'M SORRY!

SLAM!

AT OUR AGE WE ARE ALREADY A DIVIDED GENERATION. WHAT FUTURE DO WE HAVE?

HELLO, MIGUELITO. HOW HANDSOME YOU LOOK!

AND, VERY CLEAN, AS WELL. SMELL HOW CLEAN. D'YOU SMELL?

MMMMMYES

I HAVE DECIDED TO BE A GOOD MANAGER OF MY PERSON

ORTHOPAEDIC SUPPLIES, GOOD MORNING

DO YOU HAVE ANY CRUTCHES?

YES, YES, WE HAVE ALL KINDS

DO YOU HAVE ANY CRUTCHES FOR THE SOUL

FOR THE WHAT?

FOR THE SOUL!!! DO YOU HAVE ANY CRUTCHES FOR THE SOUL?

TODAY I FEEL ELOQUENT AND INSPIRED, MAFALDA

WHY, FELIPE?

BECAUSE TODAY IS CHILDREN'S DAY. A HUGELY IMPORTANT CELEBRATION WHICH IS SUPPORTED BY MANY INSTITUTIONS THAT HAVE COME TOGETHER TO ADD JOY TO ALL THE EVENTS IN WHICH CHILDHOOD IS BEING CELEBRATED ALL OVER...

GET ON! *"ELOQUENT AND INSPIRED"*. YOU GOT ALL THAT VERBIAGE FROM A NEWSPAPER

DAMNED FEMININE INTUITION... TO SEE THROUGH THINGS!

THIS MAGAZINE SAYS THAT: *"THE WIDESPREAD AWARENESS OF TECHNICAL ADVANCES IS MAKING TODAY'S CHILDREN MENTALLY MUCH BETTER DEVELOPED"*

OK, WITH SOME EXCEPTIONS...

FOR EXAMPLE?

SCRATCH SCRATCH SCRATCH

HOW DID YOU GET ON AT SCHOOL, TODAY, MAFALDA?

FINE

WE LEARNED MANY NEW THINGS

AND YOU, MAMA?

HOW WAS IT FOR YOU IN YOUR DAILY DRUDGE?

EVERY OTHER DAY THE POPE WARNS US OF THE DANGER OF WORLD WAR, BUT NOBODY PAYS ANY ATTENTION. FRANKLY, I DON'T UNDERSTAND PEOPLE

IT'S JUST THAT THEY ARE USED TO LIVING WITH THE POPE'S WARNINGS, AND THE THREATS OF WAR AND ALL THAT, MAFALDA. MAN IS AN ANIMAL OF HABITS

PERHAPS, AS A MATTER OF HABIT, MAN IS AN ANIMAL

YOU NEVER KNOW HOW IT IS WITH CATS

HOLD IT RIGHT THERE, SUSANITA

BANG!

YOU GOT ME! OH!

THE LOSS OF ONE WHO, LIKE ME, KNEW HOW TO WIN THE LOVE AND AFFECTION OF ALL WHO MET ME, HAS CAUSED DEEP SADNESS

MY DEMISE LEAVES A VACUUM DIFFICULT TO FILL IN THE MOST VARIED CIRCLES, AMONG THOSE WHO ACKNOWLEDGED MY NOBLE AND SENSITVE NATURE...

WHAT'S WRONG? WHY DON'T YOU WANT TO PLAY ANY MORE?

50

IT'S A SHAME THAT YOU HAVE TO GO TO SCHOOL, MANOLITO. YOU SHOULDN'T HAVE TO GO ANY MORE

NOOOO?

WHAT THE DEVIL ARE YOU SAYING, SUSANITA? MANOLITO AND ALL OF US MUST BE EDUCATED, BECAUSE CULTURE IS THE FOUNDATION

YES, YES! I KNOW

WHATEVER YOU SAY, MAFALDA

BUT IT IS A SHAME TO SPLASH DROPLETS OF LEARNING OVER AN AUTHENTIC OAF LIKE THIS YOUNG MAN

SO WHAT HAPPENS? ONE LEADS A LIFE, OR LIFE PUSHES YOU ALONG?

DID YOU TELL MAFALDA YET?

NO

I DON'T KNOW HOW SHE'LL TAKE THE NEWS THAT SHE'S GOING TO HAVE A LITTLE BROTHER

OH, SILLY... SHE'LL LOVE IT! IT'S JUST THAT YOU ARE A BIT NERVOUS. BETTER LEAVE IT TO ME

LET'S SEE. I'LL CALL HER CALMLY.

FAMALDA, COULD YOU COME HERE A TIMUNE

HERE SHE COMES. DO YOU THINK THIS IS THE MOMENT TO TELL HER THE NEWS THAT SHE'S GOING TO HAVE A LITTLE BROTHER?

YES, YOU LEAVE IT TO ME. I KNOW HOW TO HANDLE IT

YOU CALLED ME?

YES, MAFALDITA. COME AND SIT DOWN

SO WHY THE BOARD MEETING ATMOSPHERE?

THERE'S MANOLITO. I WONDER IF MAFALDA HAS TOLD HIM THAT SHE'S GOING TO HAVE A LITTLE BROTHER?

HELLO, MANOLITO. HAVE YOU HEARD THE GREAT NEWS?

ALMACEN 'DON MANO

HA! OF COURSE I HAVE!

IT'S THE BEST NEWS I'VE EVER HEARD. I'M VERY HAPPY

MAFALDA EVEN MORE SO

WHY? WHAT DOES SHE CARE IF THE SHOP IN THE NEXT STREET CLOSES DOWN?

WHY? **WHY** IS IT MAFALDA WHO'S GOING TO HAVE A LITTLE BROTHER, AND NOT ME?

HERE SHE COMES!

HELLO, SUSANITA. WHAT'RE YOU UP TO?

JUST... DAYDREAMING

56

WHAT I DON'T UNDERSTAND IS WHY WE HAVE TO WAIT **MONTHS** FOR YOUR LITTLE BROTHER. COULDN'T HE COME SOONER?

NO, MIGUELITO, BECAUSE PARIS IS A LOOOOONG WAY AWAY AND THE STORK THAT BRINGS BABIES HAS TO REST ALONG THE WAY. AND THAT TAKES TIME.

WHAT IF WE REACH AN ARRANGEMENT WITH AIR FRANCE?

MIGUELITO IS RIGHT, MAMA. WHY DOES MY BROTHER HAVE TO WASTE **MONTHS** TRAVELLING HERE BY STORK?

IF A JET CAN BRING, HIM FROM PARIS IN JUST 14 HOURS!

14 HOURS! DON'T YOU SEE ALL THE TIME MY BROTHER WOULD SAVE?

MY MAMA IS RIGHT, MIGUELITO. WHY THE DEVIL WOULD A BABY WANT TO SAVE TIME, IF HE HAS NOTHING TO DO ALL DAY?

HELLO, MAFALDA. WHY SO THOUGHTFUL?

NOTHING, MANOLITO. JUST THINKING ABOUT WHAT TO CALL MY FUTURE BROTHER

A NAME IS FOR LIFE, SO WE HAVE TO CHOOSE CAREFULLY AND NOT GIVE HIM THE FIRST THING THAT COMES TO MIND

NO, OF COURSE

MANOLITO!

TELL ME, MAFALDA

YOU GO AROUND WARNING AGAINST RACISM AND ALL THAT

WHAT IF THE STORK BRINGS YOU AN AFRICAN BABY! EH? HOW'S THAT? THAT'D BE NICE, WOULDN'T IT? VERY DEMOCRATIC! HA! AND WHY NOT A LITTLE AFRICAN? EH?

WHAT THE DEVIL'S THE MATTER WITH YOUR FATHER?

I WOULD LIKE SOME SWEETIES, MANOLITO, BUT I'VE GOT NO MONEY. CAN I OWE YOU?

LET ME SUGGEST SOMETHING, MIGUELITO. YOU READ THE PAPER EVERY MORNING

AND THE DAY YOU SEE THAT NO EMBASSY IS ATTACKED IN ANY PART OF THE WORLD, COME AND I'LL LET YOU OWE ME, WITH PLEASURE

THANKS, MANOLITO. YOU'RE A PAL

THE POOR THING IS EVEN MORE INNOCENT THAN I THOUGHT HE WAS

OH, MAMA! A JUMPER FOR **ME**? YOU'RE KNITTING A JUMPER FOR **ME**?

IT'S NOT FOR YOU, MAFALDA. IT'S FOR YOUR FUTURE BROTHER

AH!

IT'S ODD, BUT SUDDENLY I FEEL AS IF A SPECK OF DIRT HAD GOT INTO MY EXCITEMENT

59

WHAT A SHAME! I THOUGHT YOU WERE KNITTING SOMETHING FOR ME... BUT IT IS FOR MY BROTHER

BUT, MAFALDA, THINK OF ALL YOU HAVE ALREADY: JUMPERS, DRESSES, SOCKS, SHOES...! EVERYTHING!

ON THE OTHER HAND, YOUR FUTURE BROTHER HAS NO CLOTHES, OR ANYTHING. D'YOU SEE?

YES

IT'S LIKE BEING THE SISTER OF A REFUGEE

I SEE YOUR MOTHER IS KNITTING SOMETHING FOR YOUR FUTURE BROTHER.

THAT'S IT, SUSANITA

OF COURSE, NOW **EVERYTHING** YOUR MOTHER DOES WILL BE FOR **HIM**, RIGHT?

OF COURSE. WE HAVE EVERYTHING

BUT HE HAS NOTHING

IMAGINE, IF WHEN HE ARRIVES EVERYONE ELSE HAS EVERYTHING AND HE HAS NOTHING, HE COULD GET CERTAIN IDEAS INTO HIS INNOCENT HEAD

AND WE DON'T WANT EXTREMISTS IN THE FAMILY, DO WE?

"ACCOMPANY YOUR SPECIAL MOMENTS..."

... WITH BLACK GROG WHISKY"

PAH!

IMAGINE IF EVERY TIME WE CAME OUT OF SCHOOL WE WENT FOR A WHISKY

YOO HOO! I'M HOME, MAMA

HEY! WHAT'S THE MATTER?

NOTHING, DARLING, I'M JUST A LITTLE UPSET

THEN I'LL MAKE LUNCH FOR WHEN PAPA GETS HOME. EH? WHAT SHALL I MAKE THAT'S EASY?

PUT A PAN ON TO BOIL SOME WATER AND THROW IN ONE OF THOSE SOUP CUBES

WHAT?

SOUP

EXCUSE ME

61

SOMETIMES AT NIGHT IN BED, I START THINKING... AND IT IS STRANGE...

I FEEL, FOR EXAMPLE, LIKE EVERYBODY, THAT I HAVE MY *GOOD* SIDE AND MY BAD

AND I'M NO BETTER NOR WORSE THAN OTHERS... SO, I'M SIMPLY LIKE THE REST OF MANKIND

HAVE YOU EVER HAD THAT **HORRIBLE** FEELING?

... MARKET STREET, PLEASE?

THAT WAY FOR 3 BLOCKS, RIGHT UP TO THE CHURCH, SECOND ON THE RIGHT, CROSS THE SQUARE AND THEN YOU'LL SEE IT, MARKET STREET

AHA! THANKS

EHE?

... HAPPINESS, PLEASE?

IT'S TIME TO LISTEN TO THE NEWS

"INTERNATIONAL: ON HEARING THAT MAFALDA IS GOING TO HAVE A LITTLE BROTHER THE RUSSIANS BEGAN TO PULL DOWN THE BERLIN WALL, ARABS AND ISRAELIS...

... REACHED AN AGREEMENT, FIDEL CASTRO CALLED A GENERAL ELECTION AND THE USA AND VIETNAM BEGAN PEACE TALKS"

I'D BETTER NOT. I SUSPECT IT WILL DISAPPOINT ME

YOU SEE? IN THE END, ONLY YOU, PEPITA AND I GOT A 10 FOR DRAWING

AND REALLY THE TEACHER WAS RIGHT. ALL THREE PICTURES WERE EQUALLY GOOD, AND YOU COULDN'T SAY THAT ONE WAS BETTER THAN THE OTHERS

DAMN THE DAY I WAS TAUGHT TO BE MODEST!

63

THIS IS EXTRAORDINARY! LISTEN!

"WITH A MINUTE AND COMPLICATED TELEVISION SYSTEM INSERTED INTO THE PATIENT, DOCTORS CAN SEE INCREDIBLY CLEAR IMAGES OF THE INSIDE OF THE HUMAN BODY"

MY GOD! AND ME WITHOUT ANY MAKEUP ON THE INSIDE!

I FEEL SORRY FOR THE ARMS MANUFACTURERS

THEY CAN'T REST FOR ONE DAY, AND TO TOP IT ALL, THEIR WORK DOESN'T REFLECT WELL ON THEM

BECAUSE EVERYTHING THEY MAKE, THE ARMIES IMMEDIATELY WRECK IN WARS AND THINGS

DO YOU SEE THEIR PROBLEM?

64

HEY! WHAT IS THIS? SOME KIND OF SYMBOLISM?

NERVOUS?

65

I CAN'T WAIT FOR MY LITTLE BROTHER TO COME! ALL THIS WAITING FOR MONTHS, AND TIME NEVER SEEMS TO PASS

I UNDERSTAND, MAFALDA. THAT'S WHY IF MY PARENTS AND I WERE INTERESTED IN HAVING A NEW BABY, WE WOULD ORDER IT ANOTHER WAY

... WHAT I MEAN IS, WE'D PAY CASH, NOT INSTALMENTS LIKE YOU

I WAS UNKIND TO YOU YESTERDAY, MAFALDA. I WOULD ALSO LIKE TO HAVE A LITTLE BROTHER, EVEN IF WE HAD TO WAIT MONTHS

WHO CARES HOW LONG WE HAVE TO WAIT FOR THE STORK TO ARRIVE. WE SHOULD NOT THINK OF THAT

... BUT OF THE MARVELLOUS DAY WHEN, AT LAST, WE SEE THE STORK LANDING HERE

HA! WHAT IF JUST THAT DAY THEY STOP FLIGHTS BECAUSE OF BAD WEATHER?

FOUR MORE DAYS AND... **SPRING!**

SPRING, MIGUELITO! NOW THERE WILL BE BLUE SKIES, BRIGHT SUN, WARM TEMPERATURES, AND LOTS OF BIRDS AND FLOWERS AND BUTTERFLIES. ISN'T IT WONDERFUL?

"WONDERFUL" YEES!

CAN YOU IMAGINE HOW MUCH TAX THEY'LL WANT US TO PAY FOR ALL THAT?

BUT, MANOLITO! HOW CAN YOU BE STUCK IN THE STORE? DON'T YOU KNOW HOW MUCH SPRING THERE IS OUT HERE?

DON'T YOU KNOW HOW CLEAR THE SKY IS, AND THE SUN, AND THE FLOWERS, AND THE BIRDS AND ALL YOU CAN FEEL IN THE AIR?

FRIPPERIES!

THERE'S ONE THING I DON'T GET...

WHY DON'T **ALL** THE INHABITANTS OF THE PLANET AGREE TO LIVE HAPPILY?

BECAUSE WE ARE FOUR THOUSAND MILLION, MIGUELITO. WE'LL NEVER **ALL** BE ABLE TO AGREE

THERE ARE FOUR THOUSAND MILLION THINGS I DON'T GET...

I KNOW YOU, MANOLITO! YOU WANT TO BECOME AN EXECUTIVE...

... BUT **NOT** BECAUSE YOU'RE INTERESTED IN BEING AN EXECUTIVE, **BUT...**

BECAUSE YOU'RE A **SNOB!**

A **SWHAT?**

THE EARTH SPINS ROUND THE MOON? THE MOON ROUND THE EARTH? THEN WHY DO WE ALWAYS SEE THE SAME FACE OF THE MOON?

IT'S LIKE THIS, MIGUELITO. SUPPOSE THAT WE ARE THE EARTH AND MANOLITO THE MOON

LET'S SEE, MANOLITO. WALK AROUND THEM

THAT'S IT. VERY GOOD. D'YOU SEE? WE SPIN HERE, AND THE MOON AROUND US

... ALWAYS SHOWING THE SAME RIDICULOUS FACE

THESE DAYS WE HAVE NO REAL MEN, DON AURELIO. THAT'S WHY THINGS ARE LIKE THEY ARE!

TERRIBLE!

THOSE THINKERS! THOSE STATESMEN OF OUR DAY! THEY WERE SOMETHING ELSE! BUT THESE DAYS...! WHAT FUTURE IS THERE FOR THE WORLD IN THE HANDS OF THESE AMATEURS?

THAT'S RIGHT! WHAT FUTURE?

WHAT'S WRONG WITH THE OLD IS THEY ARE LOOKING AT THE FUTURE FROM THE BACK OF THEIR NECKS

71

ARE YOU STRUGGLING?

WELL. I'D BETTER GO AND DO MY HOMEWORK

VROOM

DAMN!

Panel 1: THAT'S IT! WE'LL PLAY COWBOYS. OK? AND THEN, SOME COMANCHES CHASE US WITH SHOWERS OF ARROWS. EH?

Panel 2: AND THEN WE SLIP UP A SECRET GULLY AND FROM THE CLIFF ABOVE, BANG!! BANG!! BANG!! BANG!! WE'LL WIPE 'EM OUT

Panel 3: LET'S GO! WOO WOO WOO!

Panel 4: HIS SCRIPTS ARE NOT BAD, BUT THEY LACK A MESSAGE

Panel 5: LOOK, MIGUELITO
WHAT?

Panel 6: THE TREES HAVE TURNED ALL GREEN
AH HA!

Panel 7: DOES THAT MEAN THAT NATURE HAS GIVEN US THE GREEN LIGHT TO CROSS TO WHERE?

OH, MAFALDA, WHAT A SWEET FRIEND YOU HAVE! TELL ME, LITTLE GIRLS, WHO DO YOU LOVE MOST? YOUR MAMA OR YOUR PAPA?

... AHEM... BOTH THE SAME

WHAT A LITTLE TREASURE!

SCHLICK
SCHLICK
SCHLICK

BLUP!

YES, I KNOW THAT...

SCHLICK
SCHLICK
SCHLICK

BLUP!

THIS GUM IS GREAT FUN AS LONG AS YOU DON'T COMPARE IT WITH ANYONE'S ILLUSIONS

WITH ALL THAT ABOUT JAMES BOND BEING SECRET AGENT ZERO ZERO SEVEN

... AND ALL THE OTHER SECRET AGENTS BEING ZERO ZERO SOMETHING OR OTHER...

... EVERY TIME I LOOK AT MY REPORT CARD I FEEL A BIT LIKE A SECRET AGENT...

LOOK, FELIPE, ON THIS SINGLE SHEET OF NEWSPAPER YOU HAVE THE TWO OPPOSITE FACES OF LIFE

ON THE ONE SIDE, THIS DOCTOR WHO WORKS FOR MANKIND...

Dr. Ricardo P. Deis, well known researcher and scientist, is looking at the most important disc...

ON THE OTHER, THIS CRIMINAL. WHAT D'YOU SAY?

LIFE SHOULD BE PRINTED ON ONE SIDE ONLY

THAT WAS OUR TELEVISION NEWS, WITH ALL THE WORLD EVENTS

THE WORLD!

IF WE WANTED TO PUT IT ON SALE, WE'D BE HARD PUT TO MAKE A CONVINCING ADVERTISEMENT

THAT'S IT! I COULD BEGIN MY ESSAY ABOUT THE DISCOVERY OF AMERICA SAYING: "COLUMBUS WAS A BRAVE SAILOR..."

PIRATES TO STARBOARD, ADMIRAL!

FANTASTIC! PREPARE FOR ATTACK!

NO! NO. I MUST THINK SERIOUSLY! LET'S SEE: "WHEN THE GREAT GENOESE NAVIGATOR ARRIVED IN AMERICA..."

O.A.S.! O.A.S.!

BAH! CHI TE CAPISCE? SPEAK CHRISTIAN, MISERABLE SWINE!

AWFUL! BETTER TO WRITE IT LIKE IT SAYS IN THE BOOK

NOT BAD, FELIPE, BUT YOU SHOULD PUT MORE IMAGINATION INTO YOUR ESSAYS

BUT... MAMA? WHEN WILL THIS BLESSED LITTLE BROTHER ARRIVE?

WHAT CAN WE PLAY?

TELL ME, MAFALDA... DID THE WORLD EXIST BEFORE WE WERE BORN?

WHAT A FOOL, MIGUELITO. OF COURSE IT EXISTED!

WHAT FOR?

TELL ME, FELIPE. SWEETIES, CARTOONS, BREAD AND BUTTER, TOYS,...

... COMIC BOOKS, CIRCUSES, BISCUITS, SLIDES, CRAYONS, CHEWING GUM AND ALL THOSE THINGS

DID THEY EXIST BEFORE WE DID?

OF COURSE

WHAT A WASTE!

WHAT DID YOU GIVE YOUR MOTHER FOR MOTHER'S DAY, MAFALDA?

A BOOK

GO ON!

REALLY, WHAT DID YOU GIVE HER?

REALLY! I GAVE HER A BOOK!

A BOOK... NOW I'M MADE TO LOOK A FOOL!

DON'T YOU THINK I KNOW YOUR MOTHER ALREADY HAD ONE?

 WHY DOES YOUR MOTHER WEAR GLASSES?

THE OPTICIAN ORDERED THEM

WHY?

 SO SHE COULD SEE WELL

SEE WHAT WELL?

 HOW DO YOU MEAN **WHAT**? **EVERYTHING!**

 AH! WAS YOUR MOTHER SUCH A PESSIMIST?

 ... AND NOW OUR EDUCATIONAL PROGRAM "LIFE IN THE JUNGLE"

 CLICK!

 IT'S ONLY TWO MINUTES SINCE THEY HIT US WITH THE NEWS!

83

KILLED HIS FRIEND TO ROB HIM!!

AMAZING HOW MUCH FITS IN THE SAME SPRING!

G'MNING, PAPA

G'MNING

G'MNING, MAMA

G'MNING

AT THIS TIME OF DAY, THERE BLOWS A CERTAIN FAMILY AIR

WE'RE FINISHING ALL THE BISCUITS, FELIPE. ANOTHER?

WELL, GREAT!

AND THE CHOLESTEROL?

HELLO, MAFALDA. DO YOU KNOW WHAT I WANTED TO TALK TO YOU ABOUT?

I HAVE MY SUSPICIONS!

WHAT DOES **THAT** "*I HAVE MY SUSPICIONS*" MEAN? WITH **THAT** FACE, EH? LET'S SEE, LADY KNOW-ALL! WHAT DID I WANT TO TALK TO YOU ABOUT? LET'S SEE! COME ON! WHAT?

ABOUT AALLLLL THE CHILDREN YOU ARE *GOING* TO HAVE WHEN YOU GROW UP!

HA! NO. IT WAS NOT ABOUT THAT! THERE YOU ARE! IT WAS NOT ABOUT THAT!

PAPA, HOW OLD ARE YOU?

37, WHY?

JUST ASKING. NO REASON

WOW, THAT'S A BIG NUMBER!

HOW ANCIENT DID YOU SAY HE WAS?

'MORNING, MANOLITO. MY MOTHER SENT ME TO SEE IF THE WHISKY YOU SELL IS DEAR

NO. IT IS NOT DEAR

IS IT IMPORTED?

NO. IT'S NOT IMPORTED

AH HA! IS IT GOOD?

EM... NNNO. IT'S NOT VERY GOOD

BUT, TELL ME. **IS IT WHISKY?**

NO, IT'S NOT REALLY WHISKY, EITHER

BUSINESS IS BUSINESS, BUT FRIENDS ARE FRIENDS

MY MAMA IS KNITTING THIS FOR MY FUTURE BROTHER

MY DARLING LITTLE BROTHER!

MY ADORABLE LITTL...

I'M WORRIED ABOUT THE FINAL EXAMS

COME ON, MANOLITO! EVERYTHING WILL BE ALL RIGHT

THOSE EXAMS ARE NOT SO BAD

IN THE END THEY ARE EASIER THAN YOU THINK

HELLO, WHAT'RE YOU TALKING ABOUT?

WHAT AWAITS US!

OH! OH! A BEE!

SHALL WE KILL IT?

NOOO. YOU DON'T KILL BEES!

AH, NO?

NO. BEES ARE GOOD AND HARD WORKING. THEY MAKE HONEY, WHICH IS HEALTHY AND TASTY

I SEE. WE DON'T KILL THEM BECAUSE THEY WORK FOR US, RIGHT?

YOU KNOW? I'VE BEEN THINKING A LOT ABOUT MY FUTURE BROTHER

AH HA!

AND I'VE REACHED THE CONCLUSION THAT IT'S BEST WE DON'T HAVE ONE

SCARED YOU!

INK

COULD YOU LET ME USE YOUR RECORD PLAYER A MOMENT? JUST TO SATISFY MY CURIOSITY

92

 LAST NIGHT I DREAMT THAT MY MOTHER SENT ME TO VISIT MY SICK GRANDMOTHER WHO LIVED IN COMMUNIST CHINA

 "TAKE THIS BASKET TO YOUR GRANNY, BUT BEWARE THE RED GUARD DOESN'T FIND YOU", MY MOTHER SAID. AND I WENT TO CHINA WITH MY BASKET

 WHEN I GOT THERE, I WAS SKIPPING HAPPILY ALONG THE STREET WHEN SUDDENLY A RED GUARD ASKED ME. "WHERE ARE YOU GOING, COMRADE"

 "I'M GOING TO VISIT MY SICK GRANNY". "AH, YES? AND WHERE DOES YOUR NICE, BOURGEOIS GRANNY LIVE?"

 COME ON! THAT'S LITTLE RED RIDING HOOD! IT'S NOT TRUE THAT YOU DREAMED IT!

 OF COURSE NOT. BUT IT'S AN INTERESTING VERSION, ISN'T IT?

 I'M SORRY, BUT MAFALDA CAN'T COME OUT TO PLAY NOW. SHE'S GOT TO DO HER HOMEWORK

JUST A LITTLE, PLEASE!

NO, NO. I SAID, NO

 WHAT IF WE KILL HER QUICKLY?

93

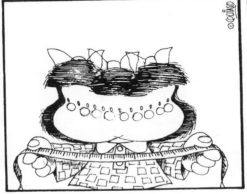

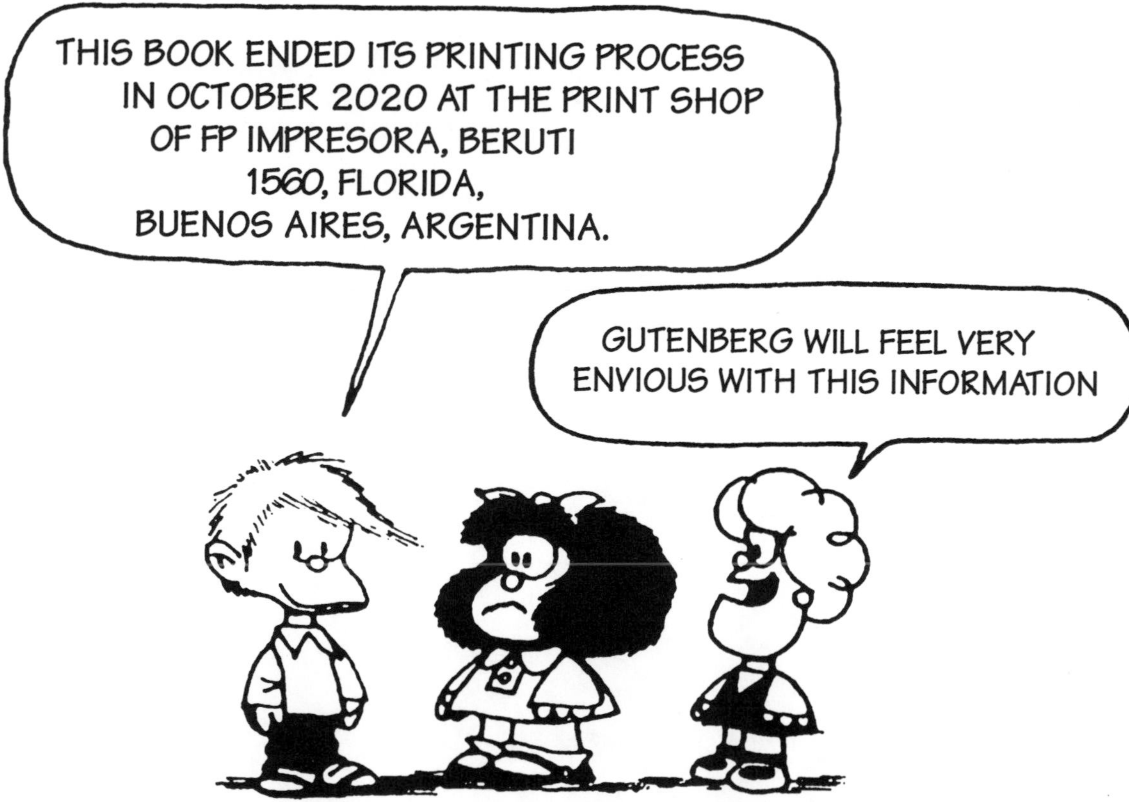
THIS BOOK ENDED ITS PRINTING PROCESS IN OCTOBER 2020 AT THE PRINT SHOP OF FP IMPRESORA, BERUTI 1560, FLORIDA, BUENOS AIRES, ARGENTINA.
GUTENBERG WILL FEEL VERY ENVIOUS WITH THIS INFORMATION